Spot is learning to count.
He goes for a walk and
meets **one** squirrel
collecting nuts to store away
for the winter.

Then he sees **two** rabbits
hiding in the grass.

Hello! Now Spot can see **three** little foxcubs.

Here come **four** snails moving slowly…

as five beautiful butterflies flutter past.

Spot looks up and counts **six** ducks flying.

Seven worms come out of their holes to see the ducks.

Spot counts **eight** frogs hopping along…

and **nine** ants crawling up a tree.

There are **ten** tiny fieldmice playing in the sun

and **eleven** little fishes swimming in the stream.

Finally, Spot counts **twelve** pretty birds and then goes home for supper.